Learning and Testing
Short Forms

A Sequence of Exercises
Graded According to
Pitman Shorthand New Course

Compiled by

J. J. WALKER, B.Com.

Deputy Principal
Balmoral State High School, Brisbane, Australia

PITMAN

PITMAN PUBLISHING LIMITED
39 Parker Street, London WC2B 5PB

Associated Companies
Copp Clark Pitman, Toronto
Fearon Pitman Publishers Inc, San Francisco
Pitman Publishing New Zealand Ltd, Wellington
Pitman Publishing Pty Ltd, Melbourne

© Sir Isaac Pitman and Sons 1966

Isaac Pitman

Reproduced and printed by photolithography,
and bound in Great Britain at The Pitman Press, Bath

ISBN 0 273 41347 3

G9–(622:24)

Introduction

IT can be universally agreed, I think, that Short Forms, and the phrases made mainly by combining them, form a large part of most commercial matter. Cold logic, then, suggests that thorough learning and practice with these forms, *from the outset*, is essential to that early mastery which makes for confident and successful facility in shorthand writing. It is to fulfil a strongly felt need for extra material that this little book has been devised. Rather than writing, practising, learning, and being tested on Short Forms as single units, students can make better progress when this learning, practice, and testing is done *in sentences*, i.e. in the normal sequence in which these forms are going to be used.

As the exercises in *Graded Dictation Studies* move forward step by step with the theory of each chapter of the *New Course*, so these sentences are also graded, in order that, when the student takes into his or her vocabulary each new set of forms, there is available material for gaining immediately a sound familiarity with these forms. To keep the learning and revising focused on Short Forms, each new list and those previously learnt form the vocabulary on which the sentences are built. The chapter numbers refer to the *New Course*.

With this sort of testing, comprehension is not at the moment the vital factor (as it is, for example, in the transcription of a business letter), because the words and their outlines *should* be so very familiar—it is just this familiarity which we are aiming to produce and test. Therefore, it should be possible for students to read the series of not necessarily connected sentences quite readily, because all the outlines should be most familiar to them, and by the same token should be clearly and legibly written.

This little work thus makes no claims to any sort of literary excellence. It is no more than what it hopes to be: a handy and practical series of exercises designed for both the student and the teacher in making sure that the basic tools of efficient shorthand writing—the Short Forms—are as well known as they undoubtedly should be, and that the process is a little more practical, efficient, and pleasant, than mere repetition work.

The sentences in the A and B exercises, respectively "For Reading and Writing Practice" and "For Writing Practice," mean just that. It is suggested that on first meeting a new list of Short Forms, some such method as the following could be adopted—

On top of a notebook page, the whole of the new list should be written *in shorthand*.

The outlines are then written in the same position along each successive line, but in a different time order. To connect sound and sign, each word is said aloud as its sign is written—

1st line ⟍ (1) ((2) ((3)) (4) ╱ (5) ╱ (6)

2nd line ⟍ (1) ((6) ((4)) (5) ╱ (3) ╱ (2)

3rd line ⟍ (3) ((2) ((1)) (6) ╱ (4) ╱ (5)

This can be changed to straight repetition for increasing speed and facility, once familiarization is complete. The page is then completed in order that complete mastery is assured.

The A and B exercises could then be worked, the sentences being written over and over until the students are confident of being able to write them from dictation.

Various methods of using the exercises will suggest themselves. It is felt that, for adequate mastery and facility, *daily* practice is essential. If, for example, there is time for only three sentences to be dictated and checked singly at the beginning of each lesson of say, 35 to 40 minutes (with perhaps two minutes given to one minute of continuous dictation and with one minute of reading back, at the end of that lesson), this daily practice should give added confidence and certainty in dealing with the general matter of, for example, *Graded Dictation Studies*. While a chapter of theory is being dealt with, it seems logical that the Short Forms based on such rules should be even more thoroughly mastered *at the same time*. Both the B and C exercises could be used for this purpose. Variety can be increased by changing the order of the sentences each time they are dictated. The "Ten-word Sentences" are specially compiled so they may be dictated at any selected speed, the ten-word size removing any need for "counting" them.

J. J. WALKER

Chapter One

SHORT FORMS ⟍ be, ⎮ it, ⎮ do, ╱ which, ⸱ the, ⟍ to, ⟍ two *or* too, ⎮ but, ⟋ who.

PHRASES ⟍ to do, ⎦ but which. With tick "the" ⟍ to the, ⟍ be the, ⎿ do the, ⎿ which the.

Chapter Two

SHORT FORMS � have, ⟨ think, ⟨ them, ⟩ was, ⟋ shall, ⟋ usually *or* usual.

Chapter Three

SHORT FORMS ▬ come, ▬ give *or* given, ⌒ him, ⌒ thing, ⟨ lord, ⟋ we.

PHRASES (Stroke "l" used to represent the word "will.") ⎿ it will, ⎿ which will, ⎿ who will, ⎰ it will be, ⎰ it will have, ⎰ which will have.

Because the vocabulary of these first three chapters is so limited, both Short Form and theory, it is felt that the respective exercises in *Graded Dictation Studies* cover amply the needs of both learning and practice of these at this stage. It is recommended that as each list of Short Forms is newly encountered, the list be written, in shorthand only, across the top line of the notebook page. Until knowledge and facility of the outlines are sure, the whole page, or more, should be completed. For the first few lines, it has been found helpful, in focusing concentration on both outline and meaning, to vary the order of writing, but not the position along the line, of each form—

.... (1) .... (2) .... (3) .... (4) .... (5) .... (6)

.... (1) .... (5) .... (2) .... (6) .... (3) .... (4)

Chapter Four

SHORT FORMS .... for, ... a *or* an, ... of, ... on, ... had.

Exercise 4A

(For Reading and Writing Practice)

1.

2.

3.

4.

5.

6.

7.

8.

9.

10.

Exercise 4B

(For Writing Practice)

1. Which of-the two of-them shall-be given it?
2. But who-will come to-give it to-the lord?

2

3. Which-was-the usual thing for-him to-give?
4. Do-the thing which-will-be usual.
5. Who had come for-them? Was-it-the lord?
6. For-them it-will-be-the usual thing to-do.
7. Have-we to-think who-will come for-it?
8. Who-will come for-it but them?
9. But shall-the lord have-to-come for them?
10. Do-we-have to-give-the thing to-him?

Exercise 4C

(For Dictation Practice—Ten-word Sentences)

1. It-was a usual thing to-be given to-him.
2. Which two of-them have given it to-the lord?
3. The thing we-have given shall-be given to-him.
4. It-will-be on-the thing we give to-him.
5. It-will-be on-the thing we usually give him.
6. Have-we given-the usual thing for-them to-do?
7. For-the two of-them it-was-the usual thing.
8. It-was usual for-the two to-think of-him.
9. Which two of-them have given him-the thing?
10. The thing had to-come but it-was for-them.

Chapter Five

SHORT FORMS ......|...... different *or* difference, ...)...... wish,
....\...... put, ...\... to be, ... owe, ... can, ... go,
.... ought, ... in *or* any.

SHORT FORM DERIVATIVES \...... being, ...L.... doing,
\...... having, ... going.

Exercise 5A

(For Reading and Writing Practice)

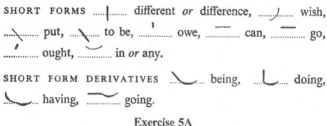

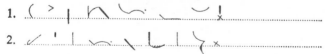

3

3.

4.

5.

6.

7.

8.

9.

10.

Exercise 5B

(*For Writing Practice*)

1. Having them do it ought-to-be-the usual thing.
2. Was-it usual for-them to-be doing it?
3. Ought we to-be doing it for-them?
4. Usually, it-will-be different for-them.
5. We owe it to-them to-be doing it for-them.
6. Ought we to-go to-him for-it to-be put on?
7. We ought to-be going, but can-we?
8. We owe it to-them to-be going, too.
9. Any wish we-can give-them ought-to-be different.
10. Being different for-them, it-will-have to-go.

Exercise 5C

(*For Dictation Practice—Ten-word Sentences*)

1. We-can do it, but it ought-to-be different.
2. Can-we two go to put it in for-him?
3. Which thing ought-to-be different for-him to-do?
4. Can-we be doing-the thing of-which we-think?
5. Ought we to-have put it in for-him, too?
6. Do-we owe it to-him to-go for-it?
7. Ought we to wish for any different thing to-do?

4

8. Any wish can usually be put in for-him, too.
9. Being different, who-can-think of-the thing for-him?
10. Having to-come was going to-be different for-him.

Chapter Six

SHORT FORMS .... are, ... our *or* hour, ... and, ... should, ... your, ... year, ... whose, ... large, ... thank *or* thanked.

PHRASE .... to go.

Exercise 6A

(For Reading and Writing Practice)

12. ....

13. ....

14. ....

15. ....

16. ....

17. ....

18. ....

19. ....

20. ....

Exercise 6B

(*For Writing Practice*)

1. Should we-thank him whose wish it-was?
2. In-which hour of-the-year was-it going to-be given to-him?
3. Any large thing should-be given to-him for-the lord.
4. Should we-do it for-him for a year?
5. Whose was-the large thing given to-him?
6. For-them it-should-be given in-any usual hour.
7. Come and give it to-him in-the usual hour.
8. The lord can give-them any wish but it-will-have to-be different.
9. Our wish was to-thank-the lord for-it.
10. It-should-be for-him and it-will-have to-be large.
11. It ought-to-be-the year for-your wish.
12. For-him to-come in for-it, it-will-have to-be different.
13. Are-we to-give-them any large thing for-the lord?
14. We-do wish them to-have it, and it ought-to-be given to-him.
15. We-are to-go to-him for-it, on-the hour.

16. It-will-be our wish to-thank them for-it.
17. Your wish can-be given to any of-them.
18. It-was-the year in-which we ought to-go for-him.
19. We-have to-do-the thing which-will-be different.
20. Your difference of an hour can-be too large.

Exercise 6C

(For Dictation Practice—Ten-word Sentences)

1. Are-we to-be thanked for-the wish given him?
2. Are-we going to-be thanked for two of-them?
3. We should-be thanked for-the hour we-have given.
4. It-was usual for-it to-be large and different.
5. Whose wish was-it to-be doing it for-him?
6. It-will-be different for-your wish to-be given.
7. We should give it to-the lord for-the-year.
8. Our going to-thank him was but-the usual thing.
9. It-was-the hour in-which we-had to-go.
10. Was-it your wish to-go for a year, too?
11. Whose wish was too large to-be given to-them?
12. Come for-your usual hour and give it to-them.
13. Can-we be different and come in for a year?
14. Whose are-the two to-be given to-the lord?
15. Come and give it to-them to-be put on.
16. Are-we to-go to-him for but a year?
17. Are-we to-be doing a different thing for-him?
18. Should-the thing in-which-we put it be large?
19. Any large thing should-be put in-it for-him.
20. It-will-be our wish for-him to-go in.

Chapter Seven
Part 1

SHORT FORMS .... ^v I *or* eye, ...∧.... how, ... [∟] why, ... [∩]

beyond, ...∩...... you, ... ^c with, ...c..... when, ... [⊃] what,

.....⊃....... would, ... ⌒ me.

7

Exercise 7A (i)

(For Reading and Writing Practice)

1. ....
2. ....
3. ....
4. ....
5. ....
6. ....
7. ....
8. ....
9. ....
10. ....

Exercise 7B (i)

(For Writing Practice)

1. You and-I can go beyond what would-be usual.
2. Would-it be usual for-your eye to-be large?
3. For-me and-for-you any wish would-be different.
4. How-can I go beyond it with-them, and why should I?
5. When shall I-have what ought-to-be given to-me?
6. Why should I go with him beyond it?
7. What can you do beyond what you-are doing?
8. How and when should-the eye be put in for-him?
9. Which eye of-the two do-you think was too large?
10. Why do-you go with-them beyond what ought-to-be?

Exercise 7C (i)

(For Dictation Practice—Ten-word Sentences)

1. For-them-the lord would-do what he ought to.
2. Beyond what you have given who-would give-the difference?
3. Why should you two go with him for-the eye?
4. With your eye, I should do it in an hour.
5. Why was-it beyond him to-do what-was usual?
6. How-can you wish to put it in-your eye?
7. Who but you would think to-give him an hour?
8. How would I come when two are going with him?
9. It-was beyond me to-give you what I ought.
10. How was I to-come when-the hour was different?

Part 2

PHRASES ⌇ I will, ⌇ I am, ⌇ I can, ⌇ can you, ⌇ give you, ⌇ with you, ⌇ when you, ⌇ what you, ⌇ would you, ⌇ are you.

Exercise 7A (ii)

(For Reading and Writing Practice)

9

9.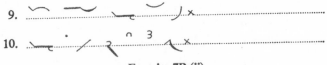

10.

Exercise 7B (ii)

(*For Writing Practice*)

1. Are-you going to-do what-you wish him to-do?
2. When-you have given what-you can I-will put in-the difference.
3. I-can come and I-shall give-you-the difference when I-do.
4. With-you in-it, I-am going to-have what I-wish.
5. Can-you have any wish for-the-year?
6. I-will-do what I-can for-your eye in an hour.
7. Are-you going when-you have him with-you?
8. Can-you come when I-am to-have-the eye put in?
9. Should I-give-you your wish, would-you thank me?
10. I-think you-should go beyond what we-have given.

Exercise 7C (ii)

(*For Dictation Practice—Ten-word Sentences*)

1. For-you I-will-do what-you ought to-do.
2. I-think I-can go with-you for an hour.
3. When-you come for an hour are-you usually thanked?
4. Can-you think what I-am to-do with-it?
5. Who-will give-you what-you wish for-your eye?
6. I-will think of what I-can do for-them.
7. When are-you going and can-you go for-them?
8. I-am to-be with-you when-you thank them.
9. I-think I usually give it to-him for-you.
10. What-you wish was put in for-him to-do.

Part 3

PHRASES ⟍ I hope, ⟍ I hope you will, ⟋⟍ we hope, ⟍ I hope you are, ⟋⟍ we hope you will, ⟋⟍ we hope you are, ⟍ he was *but* ⟍ was he.

10

Exercise 7A (iii)

(For Reading and Writing Practice)

1. ⁔⁔⁔⁔⁔⁔⁔⁔⁔⁔⁔⁔⁔
2. ⁔⁔⁔⁔⁔⁔⁔⁔⁔⁔⁔⁔⁔
3. ⁔⁔⁔⁔⁔⁔⁔⁔⁔⁔⁔⁔⁔
4. ⁔⁔⁔⁔⁔⁔⁔⁔⁔⁔⁔⁔⁔
5. ⁔⁔⁔⁔⁔⁔⁔⁔⁔⁔⁔⁔⁔
6. ⁔⁔⁔⁔⁔⁔⁔⁔⁔⁔⁔⁔⁔
7. ⁔⁔⁔⁔⁔⁔⁔⁔⁔⁔⁔⁔⁔
8. ⁔⁔⁔⁔⁔⁔⁔⁔⁔⁔⁔⁔⁔
9. ⁔⁔⁔⁔⁔⁔⁔⁔⁔⁔⁔⁔⁔
10. ⁔⁔⁔⁔⁔⁔⁔⁔⁔⁔⁔⁔⁔

Exercise 7B (iii)

(For Writing Practice)

1. I-am going to-thank him and I-hope-you-will, too.
2. We-hope two of-them are in-it for-the-year.
3. We-hope to-give and we-hope-you-will. too.
4. Which of-them was-he having for-the-year?
5. It-will-be beyond them but we-hope-you-will come.
6. Was-he in-it, and why should he be?
7. I-hope-you-are going beyond what-he-will-do.
8. We-hope-you-are thanked for what-you have given.
9. A different wish would-be beyond him.
10. He-will-be thanked but-we-hope-you-are, too.

11

(For Dictation Practice—Ten-word Sentences)

1. I-hope-you-will-do what-you can for-him.
2. He-will-be thanked for-it in a different hour.
3. I-hope he-will-think of a wish for-me.
4. We-hope it-will-be what-you wish for, too.
5. He-will-be beyond it when he can come in.
6. How-can-we do what-you wish them to-do?
7. What-do-you think we-hope-you-will-be doing?
8. Was-he to-think of what-you ought to-think?
9. In an hour he-will go with-you for-it.
10. When do-you think he-will-be going for-them?

Chapter Eight
Part 1

SHORT FORMS ⟨°⟩ as *or* has, ⟨◦⟩ is *or* his, ⟨ℓ⟩ several, ⟨ℓ⟩ those, ⟨ℓ⟩ this, ⟨ℓ⟩ thus.

NOTE ⟨⌒⟩ has the *or* as the, ⟨◦⟩ is the.

Exercise 8A (i)
(For Reading and Writing Practice)

1.
2.
3.
4.
5.
6.
7.

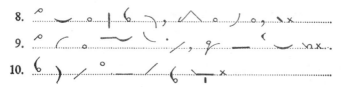

8. ....

9. ....

10. ....

Exercise 8B (i)
(*For Writing Practice*)

1. For-this year, those whose hour is different can go.
2. To-come thus, as several have, is-the usual thing in-this hour.
3. Has his hour come, for-we-think it-has?
4. The lord has his thanks to-give and has-the wishes of-those who-are going.
5. Has this thing given him his wish?
6. In an hour, he-will-think of a different thing.
7. To-thank him is-the thing you-should do.
8. That thing is as large as what-you have given.
9. Thus was-the lord going to-give to-those who would come.
10. The lord has given what-he ought, to-the two of-them.

Exercise 8C (i)
(*For Dictation Practice—Ten-word Sentences*)

1. Why-do-you think thus, of-him and of-me?
2. His wish is-the thing we-have to-think of.
3. Several of-those would-be too large for-him, too.
4. Has-the hour come for-him to-go with-you?
5. As your wish was given, you ought to-thank them.
6. Is this thing as large as what-you have given?
7. As for-this wish, it-would-be beyond him, too.
8. Would-you put those on for-me as I-wish?
9. I-think I-can give this as-the usual thing.
10. It-will-be beyond them to-do this for-him.

Part 2

SHORT FORMS ⌒ because, ⟍ special *or* specially, ⟍ speak, ⟍ subject *or* subjected.

13

NOTE The S circle is added to short forms— ⟨shorthand⟩ speaks, ⟨shorthand⟩ subjects, ⟨shorthand⟩ yours, ⟨shorthand⟩ years, ⟨shorthand⟩ ours *or* hours, ⟨shorthand⟩ things.

Exercise 8A (ii)
(For Reading and Writing Practice)

1. ⟨shorthand outlines⟩
2. ⟨shorthand outlines⟩
3. ⟨shorthand outlines⟩
4. ⟨shorthand outlines⟩
5. ⟨shorthand outlines⟩
6. ⟨shorthand outlines⟩
7. ⟨shorthand outlines⟩
8. ⟨shorthand outlines⟩
9. ⟨shorthand outlines⟩
10. ⟨shorthand outlines⟩

Exercise 8B (ii)
(For Writing Practice)

1. To-go specially to-speak to-him is our wish.
2. Beyond-the several special subjects, he-will-do these two.
3. His wish is to-go for two subjects as usual.
4. This was a special year because-he-was to-speak.
5. Because-of-this difference he-will-be specially thanked.
6. Would your eyes have to-be subjected to-this, too?
7. It-will-be subjected to what-the lord wishes.

14

8. Your wishes ought-to-be subjected to what-the lord thinks.
9. Because-of-this, you-can have a special wish.
10. Why is-he to-speak for an hour, when-the subject is beyond him?

Exercise 8C (ii)

(For Dictation Practice—Ten-word Sentences)

1. You-will-be subjected to-this thing for-several hours.
2. Several things have to-go in specially on-the hour.
3. Of-the two subjects, you ought to-speak on-this.
4. The lord is to-come specially to-speak to-him.
5. I-hope-you-will-be subjected to-the lord's wishes.
6. Two special subjects ought-to-be put in for-him.
7. Because-the lord speaks on-this subject, he-will go.
8. These special subjects are going to-be different for-you.
9. Because-we-are doing this, we ought-to-be thanked.
10. Subjected to-this, his eye was different in an hour.

Part 3

PHRASES .... for us, ... to us, ... give us.

NOTE .... when is, ... when is the, ... what is, ... what is the.

Exercise 8A (iii)

(For Reading and Writing Practice)

1. ....
2. ....
3. ....
4. ....
5. ....

15

6. *(shorthand outline)*

7. *(shorthand outline)*

8. *(shorthand outline)*

9. *(shorthand outline)*

10. *(shorthand outline)*

Exercise 8B (iii)

(*For Writing Practice*)

1. It-is usual for-several to-do what-is his wish.
2. Usually we-can think what-is-the difference.
3. Whose wish was-it to-give-us these things?
4. What-is different for-us is different for-you.
5. It-is too large for-us but he-should give it to-us.
6. He-can go with-us when-you give-us our wish.
7. Who-will go beyond it with-us?
8. When-is it to-be given for-his eyes?
9. He wishes to put in two large things for-us.
10. To-us it-will-be as large as it-is different.

Exercise 8C (iii)

(*For Dictation Practice—Ten-word Sentences*)

1. When-is-the lord going to-speak on-those subjects?
2. For-us to-thank him would-be what we owe.
3. It-is for-us to-give as-he would-do.
4. It-is usual for-them to-go in with-us.
5. Who-will think for-us and give-us our wish?
6. When-is-the hour for-them to-come to-us?
7. We-have to-think what-is-the difference to-them?
8. Why are-you with-us when-he-is in-it?
9. What-is-the thing he-will give-us for-them?
10. To-us, those subjects are as different as yours are.

16

Chapter Nine
Part 1

SHORT FORMS ....*l*.... first, ...⌢.... most, ...⌣.... influence, ...⌣.... influenced, ..⌣ₑ.. next, ...⌐.... all, ...(.... though.

NOTE ....⌢.... almost, ...(.... although, ...&.... as fast as.

Exercise 9A (i)
(For Reading and Writing Practice)

Exercise 9B (i)
(For Writing Practice)

1. He-will-have to-do all-those subjects next year.
2. His influence comes first with-them all-the-year.
3. Why is-he most different in-the first hour?
4. Though it-will-be next it-should-be first.

5. Usually he comes as-fast-as he-can.
6. Although we-thanked him most you all influenced it.
7. Almost any different thing can influence your eyes.
8. He-will-have to-do most of-those special subjects next year.
9. Though almost as-fast-as I-am he-has but two subjects to-do.
10. Although several things influence him, this-is-the first.

Exercise 9C (i)

(For Dictation Practice—Ten-word Sentences)

1. Although most things influence them this should-be-the first.
2. He-is almost as-fast-as we-are, this year.
3. All-the next year we-shall owe to-his influence.
4. It-is almost beyond his influence although he-is next.
5. Though several special things come first, he-will-be next.
6. All-these things which come first have influenced him most.
7. Next year he-will-be doing almost all-those things.
8. Almost all of-them are as-fast-as the first.
9. We-hope he-is going for most of-the-year.
10. I-think he-will come as-fast-as he-can.

Part 2

SHORT FORMS ....6.... themselves, ...9.... ourselves, ...o.... as is, ...o.... is as, ...⌒.... myself, ...⌒.... himself, ...⌐.... itself, .../.... much.

Exercise 9A (ii)

(For Reading and Writing Practice)

1.
2.
3.
4.

18

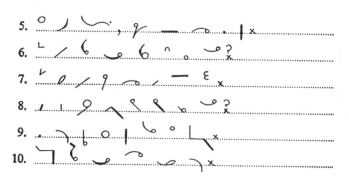

5.
6.
7.
8.
9.
10.

Exercise 9B (ii)
(*For Writing Practice*)

1. The two of-them usually thank him themselves.
2. As for ourselves we-think we should go.
3. Although he himself is doing it, we should-be.
4. Give-us those things to-have for ourselves.
5. Much of-the subject itself has to-be different.
6. We-hope-you-are specially influenced, for-we ourselves are.
7. I-myself think those things are much too large.
8. Beyond myself, who-will give him those things?
9. Should-the subject itself be much beyond me, who-will-do it?
10. To-speak on-the subject himself is beyond him.

Exercise 9C (ii)
(*For Dictation Practice—Ten-word Sentences*)

1. We ourselves are usually-the first to-go to-them.
2. I-myself think-the eye itself is much too large.
3. The subjects of-the lord are themselves to-thank him.
4. The lord himself is-as different as any of-them.
5. As-is usual with myself, I-am first to-go.
6. Much of-the difference comes when-we-do it ourselves.
7. He-is going for-it himself in-the next hour.
8. The subject itself is-as different as it-can-be.
9. Much of what I-am to-give-you comes next.
10. Can-the subjects themselves thank-the lord as-is usual?

Part 3

SW CIRCLE IN PHRASES .... as we have, ... as we think, ... as we shall, ... as we wish, ... as we may, ... as we know, ... as we can, ... as we are.

NOTE .... as well as.

SS CIRCLE IN PHRASES .... this is, ... this is the, ... this city, ... as soon as, ... as soon as possible.

SHORT FORMS .... United States, ... New York, ... largest.

SPECIAL PHRASE .... United States of America.

Exercise 9A (iii)

(For Reading and Writing Practice)

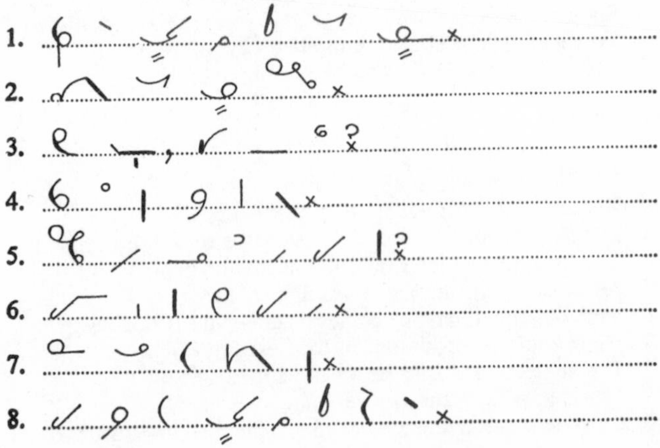

9.

10.

Exercise 9B (iii)

(*For Writing Practice*)

1. As-soon-as you-are in New-York go and-thank him.
2. We-have come to-the United-States to influence them to-**do** it.
3. Because-of-this we-speak as-we-wish.
4. The largest of-them all was too large for-us.
5. As-we-have to-go to this-city who-will come, too?
6. We-shall give as-we-think we ought.
7. As-we-shall come for-you, you ought to-go.
8. As-soon-as-possible he-will speak on-this special subject.
9. You-should all think of-us as-we-are.
10. How do I speak in-the United-States-of-America?

Exercise 9C (iii)

(*For Dictation Practice—Ten-word Sentences*)

1. As-we-are going to New-York, you-can come.
2. As-soon-as-possible we-have to-thank him ourselves.
3. Are all-these things the largest in-the United-States?
4. As-we-can-be first we-hope-you-are too.
5. It-will-be as different as-we-think it-is.
6. He-will speak for-us as-we-have to-go.
7. As-we-shall do-this for ourselves, you-should come.
8. In-the United-States-of-America this-is-the largest.
9. He-will-be influenced as-we-wish him to-be.
10. As-soon-as this-city is thanked we-can go.

Part 4

SHORT FORMS ......) especial *or* especially, ...⌣ language *or* owing, ... young, ...⌣ anything, ...⌣ nothing, ...⌣ something.

PHRASES ⏤ so much, ⏤ too much, ⏤ how much, ⏤ as much as, ⏤ inasmuch as, ⏤ as much as possible, ⏤ as early as possible, ⏤ as far as possible.

Exercise 9A (iv)
(For Reading and Writing Practice)

1.
2.
3.
4.
5.
6.
7.
8.
9.
10.

Exercise 9B (iv)
(For Writing Practice)

1. Inasmuch-as we ourselves are young, we ought to-go first.
2. How-much of-it is especially influenced by your language?
3. I-will give-you as-much-as is owing but nothing beyond it.
4. You-should all be thanked for going as-far-as-possible with him.

22

5. As-early-as-possible in-the year, anything different ought to-go to New-York.
6. It-will-be something different to-have so-much given to-us.
7. Too-much of what we ourselves do is subject to-his influence.
8. When-you do as-much-as-possible for-the young, are-you especially thanked?
9. In-the United-States, how-much is owing for-his influence?
10. Is it too-much to wish his language should-be different?

Exercise 9C (iv)

(For Dictation Practice—Ten-word Sentences)

1. As-early-as-possible this year he should give something.
2. His language, as-far-as-possible, is for-the young.
3. Nothing is too-much for-them to-do for-us.
4. Anything but this-subject would-be too-much for-them.
5. How-much is owing especially to-them in-this-city?
6. Inasmuch-as-it-is large, it-is different for-them.
7. So-much of what I-have given is too large.
8. I-hope-you-will speak as-much-as you-can.
9. He himself wishes to-give-them as-much-as-possible.
10. Nothing can influence him to-go to-the United-States.

Chapter Ten
Part 1

SHORT FORMS .... quite, ... could, ... that, ... without, ... sent, ... wished.

Exercise 10A (i)

(For Reading and Writing Practice)

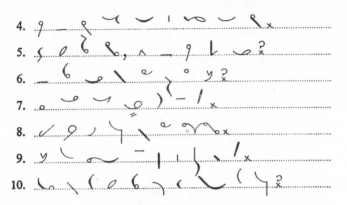

4.

5.

6.

7.

8.

9.

10.

Exercise 10B (i)

(*For Writing Practice*)

1. Could-you do without-it for an hour?
2. This-is quite a special subject on-which I-have to-speak.
3. I-have sent all-that-you wished for-this year.
4. Nothing that I-could have sent would-be any different.
5. For-us to-go without him would-be something quite different.
6. Could he have sent it beyond New-York without your influence?
7. Was-it usual for-him to-have wished for-this?
8. Although-the language was quite different he could speak it in a year.
9. I-wished that I-could speak to-him in-his language.
10. Several of-them had to-go without something for two hours.

Exercise 10C (i)

(*For Dictation Practice—Ten-word Sentences*)

1. Was-the largest of-those things sent, as I-wished?
2. Almost all-that-he wished for was sent for nothing.
3. Could-you have come without any of-that special influence?
4. As-we-are quite young we-wish to-be first.
5. Without your special influence we could-do nothing for-him.
6. When-you put anything first it-should-be quite different.

24

7. I-will-do all-that I-can to-go too.
8. I-wished to put in something quite different this year.
9. Without being sent to-do it, he thanked-the lord.
10. Could it be sent to-the United-States-of-America?

Part 2

SHORT FORMS .... ⌒ .... inform-ed, ... ⌒ .... never, November,
.... satisfactory, ... respect-ed, ... expect-ed,
.... inspect-ed-ion, ... January, ... February,
.... together, ... altogether, ... insurance.

Exercise 10A (ii)
(For Reading and Writing Practice)

25

(For Writing Practice)

1. I-informed him that-his eye would-be inspected in-November.
2. You-are respected for-your influence on-them in-January and-February.
3. Was-he informed of-the insurance inspection this year?
4. Is-it satisfactory to inspect them for insurance?
5. You and-I together could inform them of all-his wishes.
6. Why-do-we expect-the largest of-them to-come first?
7. He-will respect your wishes and-never influence them thus.
8. It-was especially satisfactory to-have all of-them together this year.
9. You-are altogether too young for an inspection this January.
10. In-November and January you-should inspect all-those who expect to-be going.

Exercise 10C (ii)

(For Dictation Practice—Ten-word Sentences)

1. I-think-the New-York inspection should-be altogether different.
2. Is-it altogether satisfactory to inform-him of-the insurance?
3. We respected his wish for an insurance inspection in-February.
4. We expect to-be together in-New-York next November.
5. January and-February are never altogether satisfactory for most insurance.
6. We expected-you to-respect his wish for-this insurance.
7. Although informed that-it-is satisfactory we should inspect it.
8. Is-it satisfactory to-speak on two subjects this November?
9. First in-January, next in-February, we all inspected it.
10. We-informed him that-it-was altogether satisfactory for insurance.

Part 3

PHRASES .... you were, ... which were, ... who were, ... they were, ... we were.

Exercise 10A (iii)

(*For Reading and Writing Practice*)

Exercise 10B (iii)

(*For Writing Practice*)

1. Things which-were first this year should-be first next year.
2. Those-who-were expected in-January ought to-come in-February.
3. We-have informed them that-you-were to-speak on-that subject.
4. They-were to-speak to-the young lord in-his language.
5. We-were going to-have them all with-us in-New-York in-January.
6. What you-were doing for-us is most satisfactory to-us.
7. Several who-were influenced most have thanked him for-it.
8. Which-were-the two things that-had to-be different?
9. They-were-the largest things that-had to-be put in.
10. We-were especially influenced because-of-his language.

27

Exercise 10C (iii)

(For Dictation Practice—Ten-word Sentences)

1. We-were specially inspected as-early-as-possible in-November.
2. Could I-be informed who-were inspected for-the insurance?
3. They-were influenced by something you-were doing in-January.
4. Which-were-the things you expected me to-give-you?
5. Without something special your influence would-be much as usual.
6. On-the subject of-the language they-were quite satisfactory.
7. You-were to-be informed on-the first of-January.
8. It-was quite satisfactory that-we-were to-be next.
9. All who-were together in-that first year are expected.
10. All-the things which-were sent have to-be inspected.

Chapter Eleven
Part 1

SHORT FORMS ...⌇.... people, ...⌇.... belief, believe, *or* believed,

....ſ.... tell, ...ſ.... till, ...ſ.... deliver, delivered *or* delivery,

....⌒.... call, ...⌒.... called, ...⌒.... equal *or* equally, ...⌒....

equalled *or* cold, ...⌇.... build, building, *or* able to.

PHRASES ....ſ.... at all, ...⌇.... by all, ...⌇.... I believe.

Exercise 11A (i)

(For Reading and Writing Practice)

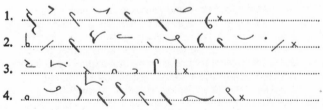

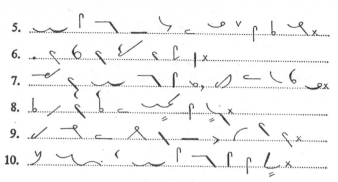

5. ....

6. ....

7. ....

8. ....

9. ....

10. ....

Exercise 11B (i)
(*For Writing Practice*)

1. Are-you able-to give any delivery at-all in-the cold?
2. I-believe he-was able-to give satisfactory delivery at-all hours.
3. Anything at-all can-be believed till he speaks.
4. Although most people call in-January, do any come in-February?
5. I-believe it-was too cold for any people to-call.
6. It-was believed equally by-all-the people.
7. It-is my belief that-he-should tell what-he-is doing.
8. Till November comes, it-should-be delivered to-the building.
9. It-is expected by-all that-he-will call to-tell-us.
10. He-will speak to-them and tell-them his beliefs.

Exercise 11C (i)
(*For Dictation Practice—Ten-word Sentences*)

1. We-believe we-were able-to tell those people something.
2. Have-we nothing cold at-all to-deliver to-them?
3. Who-were-the people called to-tell-us their beliefs?
4. Can-the buildings be inspected equally by-all-the people?
5. Tell-him we owe nothing for delivery till next November.
6. I-believe that-he-should-be thanked equally by-all.
7. Till February comes we-believe-the building is too cold.
8. I-believe people can call at-all hours for-it.
9. I-believe delivery can-be given by-all in-January.
10. Our belief is-that-he-will call and deliver it.

Part 2

<small>SHORT FORMS</small> ⟋ Dr., doctor, ⟋ dear, ⟋ during, ⟋ truth, ⟍ principal, principally *or* principle, ⟍ liberty, ⟍ member, remember *or* remembered, ⟍ number *or* numbered, ⟋ chair, ⟋ cheer, ⌐ care.

Exercise 11A (ii)
(*For Reading and Writing Practice*)

Exercise 11B (ii)
(*For Writing Practice*)

1. Has-the doctor remembered to-give equal care to all of-them?
2. What-is-the largest number of-chairs you-can put in-the building?

3. Because-it cheers him so-much, you-should remember to-care for-him.
4. The truth is-that this-city is especially cold during January.
5. How-much of-the truth of-this have-you-the liberty to-tell?
6. On principle I should tell-him that all-these chairs are too dear.
7. Think how-much it cheers him when-you put truth beyond liberty.
8. Because this-subject is dear to-the doctor he-will speak on it for hours.
9. Large-numbers of-those things are expected during that hour.
10. With care, any but-the largest chairs can-be sent.

Exercise 11C (ii)

(For Dictation Practice—Ten-word Sentences)

1. The doctor remembered to inspect his eye during-the year.
2. You have-the liberty to number-the chairs with care.
3. Which member should-be-the first to-cheer-the principal?
4. Your first care during January should-be to-cheer-him.
5. The principles of-liberty and truth come first with him.
6. This large-number of-chairs would-be much too dear.
7. It-will cheer-him for-you to-speak-the truth.
8. Have-you remembered to number all-the buildings this year?
9. The principle of truth was especially dear to-the doctor.
10. Do-you care to-give him-the liberty to-speak?

Part 3

SHORT FORMS ⌐‗‗‗ description, ⌐° surprise, ° surprised.

Exercise 11A (iii)

(For Reading and Writing Practice)

1. [shorthand outlines]
2. [shorthand outlines]

31

3. ....

4. ....

5. ....

6. ....

7. ....

8. ....

9. ....

10. ....

Exercise 11B (iii)
(*For Writing Practice*)

1. You-are expected to-give a description of-the thing as-soon-as-possible.
2. Most surprised of all was-the doctor who inspected his eyes.
3. It-is a surprise to-most people that our building is-as large as-this.
4. Next year a description of-the building has to-be sent to-the principal.
5. We-hope-you-will-be surprised when-you inspect next year.
6. All-the members expect a surprise call from-the young lord.
7. I-was surprised that your influence equalled his at-all.
8. It-is believed by-all that-he delivered all-the chairs.
9. Was-it your description of-those people that was sent to-the United-States?
10. What a surprise it-will-be when all-the members cheer!

Exercise 11C (iii)
(*For Dictation Practice—Ten-word Sentences*)

1. As a surprise, the doctor himself delivered it to-them.
2. Who-were especially surprised because-of-the cheers for-him?

32

3. I-thank-you for-your special description of-those-subjects.
4. Of-the things we-sent, which-will surprise him most?
5. Are-you surprised because-we owe so-much to-him?
6. Nothing has equalled his description of New-York in-January.
7. Should you-come in-November, it-will-be a surprise.
8. We surprised him because-he expected-you to-come first.
9. Do-you wish to-have a description of-those people?
10. We-are surprised that-you remembered our description of-him.

Part 4

SHORT FORMS .... nor *or* in our, ... near, ... own, ... owner, ... more, remark *or* remarked, ... remarkable, ... Mr. *or* mere, ... sure, ... pleasure, ... larger, ... largely, ... everything, ... over, ... however, ... respectful-ly.

Exercise 11A (iv)

(*For Reading and Writing Practice*)

1.
2.
3.
4.
5.
6.
7.

33

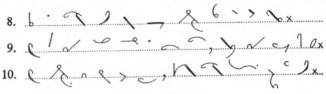

8.

9.

10.

Exercise 11B (iv)
(*For Writing Practice*)

1. Should you wish to own-the largest building, first inspect everything with more care.
2. It-is remarkable that-the owner has never come near-the building.
3. In-our own language that would-be quite a respectful remark.
4. Are-you sure that-the doctor had-the pleasure of-doing it on-his-own?
5. We-remembered his surprise over your remarkable description of everything.
6. However near to-the truth you-are we-think-you-should speak respectfully.
7. Never has-the owner himself called, nor has-he sent over any chairs for-us.
8. Largely because-of-the doctors' remarks all-the members have given with pleasure.
9. It-is more satisfactory to-be-sure all-members are equally informed of everything.
10. It gives me more pleasure to-speak to a large-number of-members.

Exercise 11C (iv)
(*For Dictation Practice—Ten-word Sentences*)

1. It-will give-them more pleasure to-do everything themselves.
2. The owners themselves are sure to-think it more satisfactory.
3. His respectful remarks are largely remembered in-the United-States.
4. A much larger building would-be too dear to own.

34

5. It-is remarkable that-he-should build without more insurance.
6. For over a year, our people largely respected his principles.
7. Are-you sure everything remembered can give pleasure to-you?
8. In-our surprise we-were influenced by a mere remark.
9. These people are sure to-respect a doctor, however young.
10. A respectful remark is sure to-give-the owner pleasure.

Part 5

SHORT FORMS ...⌒... from, ...⌒... very, ...⌒... they are, ...⌒... their *or* there.

Exercise 11A (v)
(For Reading and Writing Practice)

Exercise 11B (v)

(For Writing Practice)

1. From year to-year large-numbers of-people go there.
2. They-are very-much influenced by principles of-truth and liberty.
3. Their first wish was to-speak specially with-the doctor.
4. The subject of-his-own language was very dear to-him.
5. We-were there with him for over an hour.
6. From what-you tell-me I-shall-be-able-to surprise them.
7. Their influence on-the beliefs of-many-people is quite a surprise.
8. They-are remembered for-their very remarkable influence over him.
9. From what I-am informed I-believe all-the chairs are there.
10. Their remarks are respected equally by-the doctor and-the principal.

Exercise 11C (v)

(For Dictation Practice—Ten-word Sentences)

1. From their remarks I-believe this-subject is very satisfactory.
2. Several very different things have to-come from New-York.
3. They-are to-be thanked for-their remarkable special delivery.
4. There-are several more special calls to-come from-him.
5. The very first young-people there are remarkable beyond description.
6. From January to February their numbers are almost beyond description.
7. They-are so-much different that-we-are altogether surprised.
8. There-should-be several very different subjects during-the year.
9. They-are surprised that-their beliefs are different from yours.
10. Have-you come to-believe-the truth of-their principles?

Chapter Twelve
Part 1

SHORT FORMS ....⟍...... been, ...ℐ....... general *or* generally, ...ƒ.......
within, ...ℂ....... southern, ... northern, ...◡...... opinion.

PHRASES  had been, ⤸ have been, ⌒ more than, ⤸ better than, ⌐ larger than, ⌢⌐ smaller than, ⌐ our own, ⌐ their own.

Exercise 12A (i)
(*For Reading and Writing Practice*)

1. ....×............
2. ....×............
3. ....×............
4. ....×............
5. ....×............
6. ....×............
7. ....×............
8. ....?×............
9. ....×............
10. ....×............

Exercise 12B (i)
(*For Writing Practice*)

1. All-the members generally had-been given their-own chairs within an hour.
2. Our-own opinion is-that-the southern people have given more-than-the northern.
3. We-are more-than surprised that your building is larger-than ours.
4. We-remember when-you were smaller-than most of-them.

37

5. A larger number of-members have-been informed this year.
6. Generally an inspection is better-than a mere description of anything.
7. Southern people believe that northern people are different because-of-the cold.
8. Have-you been able-to build anything larger-than that this year?
9. February deliveries have-been better-than January deliveries this year.
10. Our-own pleasure was equal to-their-own when-he respectfully thanked all of-us.

Exercise 12C (i)

(For Dictation Practice—Ten-word Sentences)

1. In-our-opinion the northern building is more-than satisfactory.
2. It-is larger-than, and better-than, the southern building.
3. Generally our-own building has-been satisfactory for-the members.
4. This year, however, our numbers have-been more-than usual.
5. Within an hour we-expect delivery of all-the chairs.
6. In their-own opinion, his influence was smaller-than expected.
7. Generally, most people expect their-own wishes to-be respected.
8. Though quite different, our-own building is smaller-than yours.
9. All-the members believed that-their wishes had-been respected.
10. Your opinions of northern people never have-been altogether satisfactory.

Part 2

SHORT FORMS ...⌐⌐.... represent *or* represented, ...⌐⌐.... representative, ...✓.... behalf, ...⌐.... advantage.

PHRASES ...⌐.... out of, ...⌐.... number of, ...⌐.... instead of, ...⌐.... which have, ...⌐.... who have.

1.
2.
3.
4.
5.
6.
7.
8.
9.
10.

Exercise 12B (ii)
(*For Writing Practice*)

1. The number-of people who-have inspected-the building is quite a surprise.
2. Instead-of several different members, the principal representative shall speak on-their behalf.
3. His wish represents-the opinions of all-our-own members.
4. I-never believed that all-those advantages could-be expected.
5. Out-of respect for-their beliefs I-remembered to-call in-November.
6. The chairs which-have numbers on-them are for this building.
7. An inspection in-January instead-of February would-be satisfactory.
8. Something especially different is expected from-you who-have called.

9. Your representatives are expected to-speak to-the lord with respect.
10. It-will-be an advantage to-speak to-him in-his-own language.

Exercise 12C (ii)

(For Dictation Practice—Ten-word Sentences)

1. A number-of people have come out-of that building.
2. Those-who-have called are representatives of-the northern members.
3. All who speak first on-your behalf have-the advantage.
4. Who-is-to represent our members instead-of-the doctor?
5. The chairs which-have-been sent are all quite satisfactory.
6. To-speak in their-own language will-be an advantage.
7. Instead-of being your representative he called on-their behalf.
8. Out-of those-who-have represented us, he comes first.
9. I-think your general remarks surprise a number-of representatives.
10. It-is a pleasure to-speak on behalf of-liberty.

Part 3

SHORT FORMS .... gentleman, ... gentlemen, ... cannot, ... told, ... tried, ... trade *or* toward, ... third.

PHRASES .... had not *or* do not, ... did not.

Exercise 12A (iii)

(For Reading and Writing Practice)

40

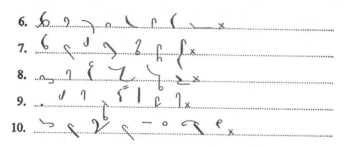

6.

7.

8.

9.

10.

Exercise 12B (iii)

(*For Writing Practice*)

1. I-believe you tried everything in-your wish to cheer-the gentleman.
2. Our United-States trade in-January was very satisfactory.
3. These gentlemen should-be told-the truth of-our opinions.
4. The owner cannot expect more-than usual care to-be given.
5. Towards January, we-remembered we-had-not delivered-the chairs.
6. Those remarkable people did-not expect to-be third.
7. However respectful he tried to-be, the owner did-not thank him.
8. You cannot expect-the doctor to-remember what-he had-not-been told.
9. Do-not expect our trade with New-York to-be equalled this year.
10. Have-you tried to-go beyond-the United-States for trade?

Exercise 12C (iii)

(*For Dictation Practice—Ten-word Sentences*)

1. This gentleman was told that-the doctor cannot represent him.
2. All-these gentlemen do-not believe-that trade is satisfactory.
3. I-think that-we tried most in-the third year.
4. We-did-not expect him to-call there till November.
5. He had-not usually been quite respectful towards these gentlemen.

41

6. Although he-was third, he tried specially to-be first.
7. We told-them that-we trade with-the United States.
8. We-do-not expect any gentleman to-give his opinion.
9. You-cannot expect anything to-be given towards-that building.
10. You had-not remembered-the principal advantage of-building insurance.

Part 4

SHORT FORMS .... |...... difficult, .|........ difficulty, ... balance, ... balanced, ...∧.... responsibility, responsible, ...⌐...... great, ... guard, ...⌐.... gold.

PHRASE .... at once.

Exercise 12A (iv)
(*For Reading and Writing Practice*)

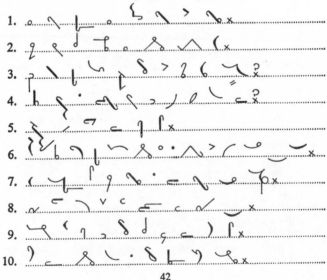

42

(For Writing Practice)

1. Because-we respected your difficulties, we delivered-the gold at-once.
2. The balanced remarks of-the doctor represent-the opinions of-most responsible members.
3. Who-will guard all-the gold sent to-the United-States?
4. Is-it any great difficulty to-be responsible for-the truth of-your remarks?
5. You-are expected to guard-the principle-of liberty with great-care.
6. More gold can-be-sent to-balance the difference in trade.
7. It-will-be a great advantage to-be informed of-our responsibility at-once.
8. You-are responsible for having-the chairs delivered next.
9. We-balanced the truth of-our remarks with respect for-his-opinions.
10. Can-you come at-once to guard-the building for-the owner?

Exercise 12C (iv)

(For Dictation Practice—Ten-word Sentences)

1. It-is our responsibility to guard-the gold at-once.
2. Generally the guards speak to-the owner with great respect.
3. With care, we-can expect a trade balance in-November.
4. This great difficulty cannot-be given to-him at-once.
5. We expect-the balance of-the subject to-be difficult.
6. Are-you responsible for-the insurance of-all-this gold?
7. It-is-the lord's responsibility to inspect-the guard, too.
8. With respect, he-should give-the members a balanced opinion.
9. Our own difficulties are very-great because-of-the cold.
10. It-was difficult to guard all-the gold at-once.

Chapter Thirteen

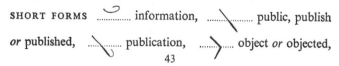

SHORT FORMS .... information, ... public, publish *or* published, ... publication, ... object *or* objected,

....⟩.... objection, ...⟍⌐... organize *or* organized, ...⟍₆.... organization, ...ʃ.... satisfaction, ...⟍ₑ.... investigation, ..⟋... yesterday.

Exercise 13A
(*For Reading and Writing Practice*)

1.
2.
3.
4.
5.
6.
7.
8.
9.
10.

Exercise 13B
(*For Writing Practice*)

1. Can these gentlemen influence public opinion to-the satisfaction of-our organization?
2. However respectful your representative was, the owner objected to any information being given.
3. Our object is-to organize a public investigation as-soon-as-possible.
4. Almost from-the first, people remarked on-the information published in-this publication.

44

5. Was there any objection yesterday to-the publication of-the objects of-our organization?
6. It gives great satisfaction to publish this remarkable information.
7. Organized trade was influenced yesterday owing-to large deliveries of-gold.
8. Your objection to an organized investigation surprised the members.
9. Any publication of-the owner's remarks is sure to-give him satisfaction.
10. Yesterday we published-the first description of-this remarkable building.

Exercise 13C

(For Dictation Practice—Ten-word Sentences)

1. Why-do-you object to-the publication of-this information?
2. In-our publication yesterday we called for a special investigation.
3. Is-this organization of any satisfaction to-the general public?
4. Information published yesterday influenced several-people to-speak their objections.
5. Can-you organize publication of-the balance of-this information?
6. Because-of-our objection, you-cannot publish this different information.
7. Because-of several special objections, an investigation was organized yesterday.
8. Has-the owner objected to an inspection from our organization?
9. We-were-the very first to publish this remarkable information.
10. A public investigation is sure to-be called for next.

Chapter Fourteen

SHORT FORMS ..⟋.... whether, ...⌒.... important *or* importance, ..⌒.... improve, improved *or* improvement, ...⌒.... impossible,

.......⌐..... child, ...?..... chaired, ...?.... cheered, ...⌐.... accord, according, *or* according to, ...⌐.... cared, ...⌐.... particular, ...⌐.... opportunity.

Exercise 14A
(*For Reading and Writing Practice*)

1.
2.
3.
4.
5.
6.
7.
8.
9.
10.

Exercise 14B
(*For Writing Practice*)

1. It-is-important that-you-should remember-the January inspection.
2. This represents a remarkable opportunity for a young child to-improve his language.
3. According-to our beliefs truth and liberty are of particular importance.

4. I-was surprised that-he cared to-represent-the northern members.
5. Whether he-was respectful is more-than I-can-remember.
6. Delivery in-the cold of November is difficult but never impossible.
7. All-the people cheered when their representative was thanked in public.
8. Should-the owner have chaired-the investigation of-his-own building?
9. What particular advantage is-it to-have more subjects this year?
10. What special opportunity would-you expect-the child to-have?

Exercise 14C

(For Dictation Practice—Ten-word Sentences)

1. I-believe that-this-is an opportunity of particular importance.
2. According-to our information an improved publication is quite impossible.
3. We-were cheered because-of-the improvement in-the child.
4. You never cared whether a responsible member chaired our organization.
5. Can-we publish this important information at-the first opportunity?
6. I-am surprised that-this particular child remembered to-call.
7. According-to their beliefs all-the members cheered their representatives.
8. Whether-the doctor chaired-the investigation was-the members' responsibility.
9. In-our-opinion it-is-impossible to inspect everything published.
10. Everything was cared for equally according-to your first wish.

Chapter Fifteen
Part 1

SHORT FORMS .... short, ... hand, ...under, ... yard, ... word, ... immediate, ... school,

.... schooled, ... spirit, ... certificate, ... knowledge, ... acknowledge.

PHRASES .... if it, ... if it is, ... in which it is, ... I am not, ... you are not, ... you will not, ... you were not, ... this would be.

Exercise 15A (i)
(For Reading and Writing Practice)

1. ....
2. ....
3. ....
4. ....
5. ....
6. ....
7. ....
8. ....
9. ....
10. ....

Exercise 15B (i)
(For Writing Practice)

1. Because you-are schooled in-the language of-the people you-should acknowledge their beliefs.
2. A short description is all-the information we care to publish.

3. You-were-not on hand when-we-were informed of-their great difficulty.
4. As-soon-as we-have your insurance certificate, immediate delivery can-be given.
5. You-are-not to publish-the information till we-give-the word.
6. The building in-the school yard should-be inspected this January.
7. You-will-not surprise him because-he remembers this from-his school.
8. Your knowledge of-our trade with-the United-States is remarkable.
9. I-am-not sure that-this-would-be according-to-the spirit of-your organization.
10. According-to his description the gold is under-the building.

Exercise 15C (i)

(For Dictation Practice—Ten-word Sentences)

1. I-acknowledge with pleasure-the remarkable spirit of-your school.
2. Because-of-the doctor's knowledge he-can give a certificate.
3. The owner expects immediate delivery to-his particular building yard.
4. The gold for-the United-States was sent under guard.
5. Has-the representative given-the members any word of-cheer?
6. This-would-be too short to-be called an investigation.
7. If-it-is possible you-should number all-the chairs.
8. Do-you remember-the publication in-which-it-is published?
9. You-will-not object to information published at first hand.
10. I-am-not surprised that-you-were-not there yesterday.

Part 2

SHORT FORMS .... character, ... wonderful *or* wonderfully, ... rather *or* writer, ... therefore, ... interest.

49

PHRASES ⌣ in their, ⌎ have their, ⌐ I am sure there is, ⌐ some other, ⌐ my dear sir, ⌐ my dear madam.

SPECIAL PHRASES ⌐ in order that, ⌐ in order to, ⌐ rather than, ⌐ not later than, ⌐ no longer than, ⌐ this letter.

Exercise 15A (ii)
(*For Reading and Writing Practice*)

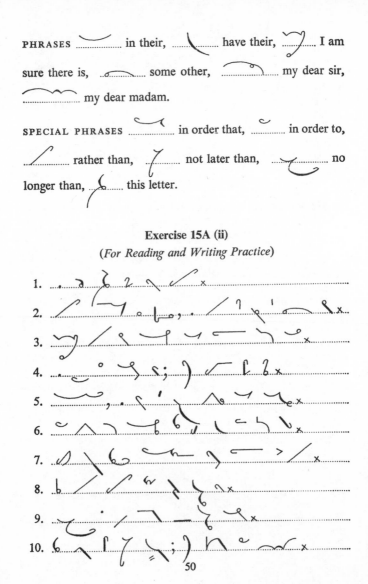

1. x
2. x
3. x
4. x
5. x
6. x
7. x
8. x
9. x
10. x

Exercise 15B (ii)

(*For Writing Practice*)

1. Rather-than believe-the writer he inspected-the building himself.
2. I-am surprised that a publication of-this character should interest-you.
3. I-believe that this-is a rather wonderful opportunity for-him.
4. The inspection was satisfactory; therefore we-have-sent everything for-the building.
5. In-their great difficulty the people wished to-have-their representative call.
6. I-am-sure-there-is some-other opportunity for trade with New-York.
7. In-order-that satisfaction can-be given you-should deliver it as-early-as-possible.
8. This-letter should-be sent not-later-than-the next hour.
9. In-order-to cheer him, my-dear-sir, you-should call as-soon-as you-are expected.
10. The general opinion is-that he should-be no-longer-than an hour.

Exercise 15C (ii)

(*For Dictation Practice—Ten-word Sentences*)

1. I-am-sure-there-is wonderful interest in-your publication.
2. The writer can speak for no-longer-than an hour.
3. In-their-opinion the doctor was a gentleman of-character.
4. I would rather have delivery not-later-than next November.
5. He-has improved wonderfully; therefore we owe him a certificate.
6. In-order-to interest them, we tried everything we could.
7. You-will-be interested in-the publications of-this writer.
8. We-believed this remarkable information because-of-his responsible character.
9. The owner expected this-letter; therefore it-cannot surprise him.
10. We numbered it in-order-that-it-would-be remembered.

Chapter Sixteen
Part 1

SHORT ·FORMS .... commercial-ly, ... inscribe-**d**, ... inscription, ... instructive, ... instruction, ...circumstance, ...signify-ied-icant, ...significance.

Exercise 16A (i)
(For Reading and Writing Practice)

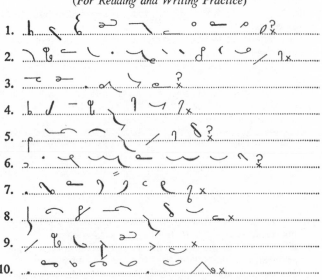

Exercise 16B (i)
(For Writing Practice)

1. In-the circumstances it-is-difficult to-deliver all-the information.
2. The principal believes that-the inscription on-the building should-be larger.

3. A special publication has-been published for-the instruction of owners.
4. The members will all signify their pleasure with cheers.
5. The principal advantage of-this building is its commercial importance.
6. The instructive remarks of-the doctor influenced the young child.
7. It-will-be too-dear to-have all-the chairs inscribed with numbers.
8. What-is-the significance of-the words in-the school certificate?
9. It-is rather significant that-the principal objected to-this organization.
10. The character of-the instruction given in-this school has improved wonderfully.

Exercise 16C (i)

(*For Dictation Practice—Ten-word Sentences*)

1. The principal acknowledges-the important significance of a commercial certificate.
2. We inspected-the first inscription with great surprise and pleasure.
3. You-should-have remembered-the instructions given in-that publication.
4. The owner's satisfaction should-be immediately signified by his certificate.
5. In-these circumstances anything inscribed in-his language is important.
6. Do-you remember-the instructive remarks delivered by-the doctor?
7. Is-it significant that-he tried to-trade in-February?
8. His interest in larger buildings is commercially significant for insurance.
9. Any inscription inscribed on-his certificate cannot improve his satisfaction.
10. Under those circumstances the doctor's instructions are difficult to-remember.

Part 2

 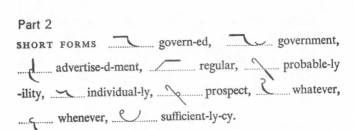 govern-ed, government, advertise-d-ment, regular, probable-ly -ility, individual-ly, prospect, whatever, whenever, sufficient-ly-cy.

Exercise 16A (ii)
(For Reading and Writing Practice)

1.
2.
3.
4.
5.
6.
7.
8.
9.
10.

Exercise 16B (ii)
(For Writing Practice)

1. I-believe in-the importance of-sufficient, regular advertise-ment.
2. Are-you sufficiently informed of-the prospects of-this remarkable school?

54

3. In-all-probability they-were-able-to inform individual members yesterday.
4. Whenever governments acknowledge-the prospect of difficulty, people generally are equal to-it.
5. The sufficiency of-his-knowledge governed-the words of-the writer.
6. Whatever you advertised probably could-be of general interest.
7. Regular trade with your government is probably quite difficult.
8. Individual members speak respectfully whenever-the doctor is in-the chair.
9. Your remarks should-be governed by whatever instructions you-were given.
10. We-acknowledge that-there-is a sufficiency of-advertisements published this year.

Exercise 16C (ii)

(For Dictation Practice—Ten-word Sentences)

1. Whenever you have an opportunity you-should advertise this publication.
2. It-is probable that-we-can influence him sufficiently ourselves.
3. The individual characters of-the members can probably be improved.
4. The principal governed-the school with regular and sufficient care.
5. This remarkable advertisement improved-the prospects of-the organization wonderfully.
6. Whatever-the probability of-improvement, more instruction is quite important.
7. Regular government inspection of all-those buildings cannot-be organized.
8. A sufficiency of public interest in government publications is expected.
9. Whenever there-is sufficient government advertisement, public interest is satisfactory.
10. Whenever people believe in liberty, individual public responsibility is improved.

Chapter Seventeen

SHORT FORMS 　danger,　　financial-ly, mortgage-d,　neglect-ed,　practice-se-d, university,　English,　exchange-d, familiar-ity,　telegram.

Exercise 17A
(For Reading and Writing Practice)

Exercise 17B
(For Writing Practice)

1. You-should-have an insurance certificate when-the building is-to-be mortgaged.
2. Because-he had practised with great-care, there-was never any danger.

3. We-were surprised that-the Government neglected to-improve-the university.
4. Your regular financial advertisement is quite familiar to-the general public.
5. Because-of-your familiarity with English practice we-expect-you to organize-the trade.
6. Can-we exchange those chairs without much difficulty?
7. You-should remember-the danger-of neglected opportunities.
8. Generally he-will acknowledge any telegram that-is sent to-him.
9. In-the University you-are expected to-exchange information.
10. You-should practise-the difficulties of-the language as-much-as-possible.

Exercise 17C

(For Dictation Practice—Ten-word Sentences)

1. Are-you familiar with financial practice in an English university?
2. You-should practise speaking with great familiarity on-those subjects.
3. A telegram to-the owner could influence-the next mortgage.
4. Have-you exchanged your principles for any more-important beliefs?
5. There-is financial danger when-you neglect important commercial opportunities.
6. Is-it regular practice to-exchange representatives with-the University?
7. To-practise difficult words should give familiarity with-the language.
8. You as owner are responsible for neglect of-the mortgage.
9. Are-you familiar with English opinion towards more building insurance?
10. A telegram should tell-him of-his danger at-once.

Chapter Eighteen

SHORT FORMS .... inconvenience-t-ly, ... distinguished, ... income, ... become, ... becoming, ... welcome, ... nevertheless.

57

Exercise 18A

(*For Reading and Writing Practice*)

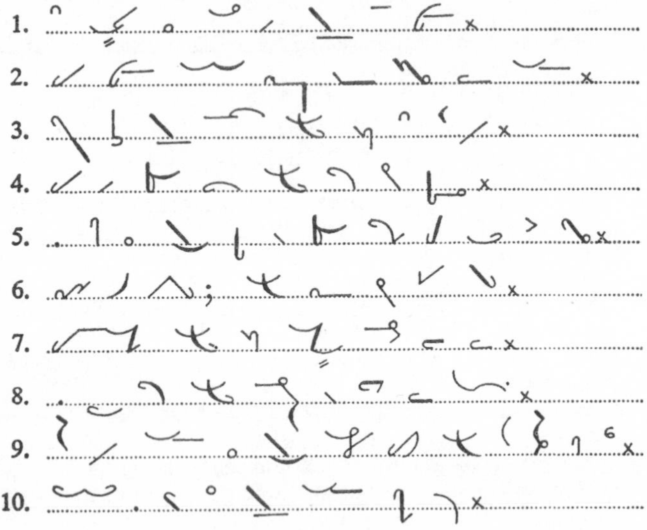

Exercise 18B

(*For Writing Practice*)

1. As ail-the members cheered, the distinguished writer acknowledged-the welcome.
2. It-is becoming more inconvenient to-deliver this publication to all-our members.
3. Something that-is a mere inconvenience could become a great danger.
4. Although you think November is cold, it can nevertheless be distinguished from January.
5. The wonderful welcome surprised and cheered him.
6. The income of-your organization ought-to-be published because-it represents public information.
7. To guard-the members from inconvenience we-have-sent more-than sufficient chairs.

8. Although it-is inconvenient for-him, nevertheless he-should thank-you.
9. Because-of language differences it-is becoming difficult to-trade with-them.
10. Should our regular income be distinguished from that of the northern members?

Exercise 18C

(*For Dictation Practice—Ten-word Sentences*)

1. Although you objected to-our organization, nevertheless you-are welcome.
2. Can-you distinguish-the inscription on-the University without inconvenience?
3. We welcome anything that can probably improve our income sufficiently.
4. It-is becoming quite inconvenient to-exchange anything for gold.
5. He-has become quite a familiar character in-our organization.
6. There-will-be a special welcome for our distinguished representatives.
7. It-has become more difficult to-improve our income sufficiently.
8. It-is becoming more difficult to-give a satisfactory certificate.
9. You rather inconveniently expected me to-be present there yesterday.
10. I can generally come, but nevertheless it-is an inconvenience.